The Grunts

written by Jon Buxton

illustrated by Andreas Grünthaler

Just past your house
and along the road,
Go down the next lane
and follow your nose.

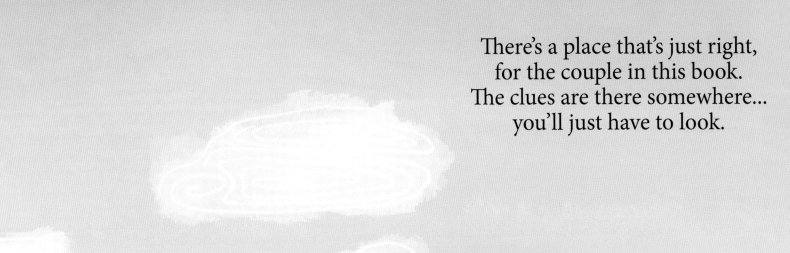

There's a place that's just right,
for the couple in this book.
The clues are there somewhere...
you'll just have to look.

You'll rarely meet a Grunt,
and there's a simple reason why...
She doesn't like attention
and he's extremely shy.

They spend their time together,
doing things you wouldn't believe,
Moving great big boulders,
with a push and a grunt and a heave.

They're as big as your bed,
with hair that is knotted,
They don't tend to brush it
as they never get spotted.

To give it a wash,
would be truly absurd,
As it's home to a spider,
a frog and a bird.

You can come across their hair
which has caught on bits of wire,
Or on the ends of branches
if you look a little higher.

The Grunts can hide and disappear,
using bushes, rocks and trees.
You can sometimes smell their scent
as it travels on the breeze.

He has powerful shoulders,
she has powerful thighs.
Their body type is of a thicker set,
both are comfortable with their size.

They've always worked well together,
preferring the late of night.
They helped a bit at Castlerigg
to get the stones up right.

They put them out for us to use,
to climb or take a rest...
But the noise they hear from playing kids
is what the Grunts like best.

They'll dump a boulder in a field,
then in the hours after,
They'll hide behind a tree or wall
and listen to the laughter.

They move along in silence,
never to make a sound,
But the problems begin,
when they're faced with a thing,
that requires a step off the ground.

The Grunts are a little bit heavy,
which can cause them to regularly fall,
When out in the dark, whilst crossing a fence,
or trying to climb up a wall.

You can see where they've been,
by the walls which are trampled,
Or the fences and gates
which are broken and tangled.

This isn't done on purpose,
with that there is no doubt.
It's the hinges, locks and latches
that they struggle working out.

The Grunts are kind and caring,
though there's sadness in their eyes;
They longed to start a family,
but that time has passed them by.

This doesn't get them down
or make them feel annoyed.
That's why they place the boulders out,
to try and fill the void.

The boulders can vary in sizes,
and some are even well known,
Like the one that they pushed down at Keswick,
which was named as the Bowder Stone.

So they leave them out in places,
where they think we'll likely pass.
You'll find them in the woodlands,
or in the fields amongst the grass.

If you come across a boulder,
when on a local expedition,
There's a good chance that the Grunts have
played a part in its position.

Now a question which arises,
and what many people ask,
Is "How on earth have they moved them all?
It's surely an impossible task."

When it comes to moving boulders,
the Grunts are considered elite,
But they've also been helped considerably
by a large-scale glacial retreat.

A long time ago the earth got cold,
and the ends would sometimes freeze.
The ice would move as a glacier,
picking boulders up with ease.

The glaciers would carry the boulders,
and move them all around.
Then as it got warmer, the ice would melt,
and leave them on the ground.

So think of the Grunts,
when you next pass a boulder...
Perhaps take a look,
or the time to come over.

They'll be pleased if you stop,
they'll be pleased if you play.
They'll be listening for laughter,
which will surely make their day.

To my five year old boy, who tells me "I like the other one better."

First published in the UK in 2023 by

Puddlebrush Books ®
Lake District Tales of Nature

Printed in England

ISBN 978-1-8384538-2-4
Text copyright © Jon Buxton 2023
Illustrations copyright © Andeas Grünthaler 2023

Paper used by Puddlebrush Books is made from wood grown in sustainable forests.